This book belongs to

_____

Join Mr. Fogherty on a tale of adventure, romance, and relaxation.
Get your feet wet as you paddle through this watery collection of pen-and-ink
illustrations all waiting to be brought to life through color.

A frog of distinction, Mr. Fogherty made his debut in the R.J. Hampson Coloring Book
'Night Garden'. His continued popularity is now rewarded with 'A Frog's Tale' which is
dedicated entirely to this enigmatic amphibian and his many friends.

For artists, coloring enthusiasts, and frog lovers of all ages!

See more at rjhampson.com

 russelljamesart

Published by Hop Skip Jump
PO Box 1324 Buderim Queensland Australia 4556

First published 2023.
Copyright © 2023 R.J. Hampson.

ISBN: 978-1-922472-20-5

hopskipjump®

Using this book

Find a quiet place away from distractions. Relax and immerse yourself in the process of coloring as you explore the details of each fantastic illustration.

This book is best suited to color pencils or markers. Wet mediums should be used sparingly. Slide a card or sheets of paper behind the illustration you are coloring to avoid marker bleed through.

Find fresh coloring pages by signing up to Russell's newsletter. Get free downloadable pages and updates on new books at -

rjhampson.com/coloring

REST & RECREATION

ORIENTATION

MORNING TEA

BEAUTIFUL DAWNING

A PURPOSE IN LIQUIDITY

A FRIEND IN NEED

THE INFERNAL COMBUSTION ENGINE

THE PARLOUR WALL

RIVER DREAMING

STOAT'S QUALITY HATS

EN PLEIN AIR

ESCARGOT

PUB LUNCH

MR. FOGHERTY FALLS ASLEEP

CHARMED

NEMESIS

ROYAL RESIDENCE

ROYAL AUDIENCE

MUSICAL INTERLUDE

A SPOT OF INVENTING

FLIGHTS OF FANCY

THE TOURNAMENT

PROMENADE

AN EVENING'S REPOSE

NIGHT SONG

Time for more?

Find new coloring pages by signing up to R.J. Hampson's newsletter.
Get free downloadable pages, monthly coloring sheets,
and updates on new books at -

rjhampson.com/coloring

Thanks for choosing this coloring book.
If you enjoyed it, please consider leaving a review.
It will help to let more people in on the experience
plus you'd certainly make this illustrator very happy!

Published books in this series

See flip-throughs and new releases at **rjhampson.com**

Printed in the USA
CPSIA information can be obtained
at www.ICGtesting.com
LVHW072144021023
759827LV00087B/223

9 781922 472205